Penguin Books
The New Penguin Calman

Mel Calman was born in London in 1931 and educated at
the Perse School, Cambridge, St Martin's School of Art and
Goldsmith's College, London. He has worked as a cartoonist
for the *Daily Express*, *Observer*, *Sunday Telegraph* and in
television, publishing and advertising. He now draws
regularly for the *Sunday Times*. Apart from his free-lance
work he runs an art gallery, The Workshop, that
specializes in cartoons, graphics and illustrations. He has
made an animated film, *The Arrow*, for the British Film
Institute and has written for magazines in Great Britain and
the United States. His daily feature, 'Men and Women', is
syndicated in America.

Mel Calman's other books include *My God* and *This
Pestered Isle*, and contributions to two anthologies, *The
Evacuees* and *All Bull* (edited by B. S. Johnson). He is
married to the artist Karen Usborne and they live in
London with his children, her children and their cat.

Mel Calman

The New Penguin
Calman

Penguin Books

Penguin Books Ltd, Harmondsworth,
Middlesex, England
Penguin Books, 625 Madison Avenue,
New York, New York 10022, U.S.A.
Penguin Books Australia Ltd, Ringwood,
Victoria, Australia
Penguin Books Canada Ltd, 2801 John Street,
Markham, Ontario, Canada L3R 1B4
Penguin Books (N.Z.) Ltd, 182–190 Wairau Road,
Auckland 10, New Zealand

Bed-sit first published in book form by Jonathan Cape 1963
'Troubles with my Aunt' first appeared in the *Daily Telegraph Magazine* 1974
Calman & Women first published by Jonathan Cape 1967
'The Resident' first published in *The Penguin Mel Calman* 1968
Couples first published in book form by The Workshop 1972
This collection first published 1977

Designed by Philip Thompson

Copyright © Mel Calman, 1963, 1967, 1968, 1972, 1974, 1977
All rights reserved

Made and printed in Great Britain by
Richard Clay (The Chaucer Press) Ltd., Bungay, Suffolk
Set in Monotype Modern Extended

For Stephanie, Claire,
Ashley and Susanna...

Bed-sit

'Bed-sit' first appeared in the Sunday Telegraph *in 1962*

It may be small but the proportions are pleasing . .

Which is it to be today?
Toast and music,
toast and light,
music and toast in
darkness,
toast in silence?

*Have you
ever tried
to barbecue a
lamb chop
on a
gas ring?*

*The annoying thing about these rooms is that you
can almost overhear*

Some of my best friends are acquaintances

*There comes a time in every bachelor's life
when he must say:
no more beans on toast –
and mean it*

The landlady doesn't like the word 'restrictions'. She calls them 'aids to communal living'

*I usually go
to the
launderette
in Kensington –
you meet a
better class
of dirty
washing there*

*That's funny – I didn't
know they
even knew each other*

*I could be
very
dominating –
if only
someone
would
volunteer to
be submissive . . .*

*I think I'll
ring
the office
and say
I'm dead . . .*

*I like to give the suit
an airing
from time to time*

*The girl next door
never seems to run out
of anything*

The score is
highly gratifying:
Christmas cards sent: 30
Christmas cards received: 32

Paper hat, yes.
Balloon, yes.
Bottle, yes.
Now let revelry commence . . .

*Gentleman with artistic tastes
and cold feet
wishes to meet lady with
property in Bermuda . . .*

We depressives
are entitled
to a little bit
of manic
now and then . . .

Troubles with my Aunt

1. *Paper Bags*

My aged Aunt saves paper bags. I don't mean that she puts one or two away in a drawer for a rainy day. We all do that. I mean she keeps every single paper bag that comes into the house. She unwraps the bread and carefully puts the bag in a drawer. She places the bags from the groceries in the same drawer. She has a system: the brown bags in one drawer and the white bags in another drawer.

She usually puts the small bags inside the largest bags, to save space. Bags lie on top of bags. Bags nestle inside bags. Bags beget bags. Whole communes of bags live inside those kitchen drawers.

I ask my Aunt, when I feel slightly frayed by all this bag cupidity, why she keeps all these bags. 'I need them,' she says, and the subject is closed. To be fair to her, she does use some of the bags. Let me explain.

Every night my Aunt prepares her bedtime tray. This tray is a ritual, an appeasement to the gods of sleep. The pink tray is placed beside the kitchen sink. My Aunt carefully takes three cups and half-fills them with cold water. Always three cups, always the same three cups. And always half-full. Never three-quarters or five-eighths. Exactly half. They are half-full because my Aunt has worked out over the years that a half-cup is exactly the right amount she needs to ease her heartburn. She gets attacks of heartburn in the middle of the night and she drinks fruit salts for this. A full cup of fruit salts is too much of a good thing. And she needs this cure three times a night. Hence, the three cups.

Ah, you may ask, why not a jug and three empty cups? Or even, a jug and one cup, which then gets half-filled three times? Because, as my Aunt patiently explained to me once, this method is foolproof and ready for use. It's an instant heartburn kit. No messing about in the half-light, trying to half-fill cups.

I once bought a jug and tried to persuade her to change her system, and she gave me a long, level stare that said: Never meddle with the laws of nature . . .

What about the paper bags, you cry. How do the paper bags cure the heartburn? Has the man lost all sense of narrative shape and decency? No. The paper bags are carefully torn open, flattened and used to cover the cups (or half-cups) of water. Each half-cup has its own little nightcap of paper, held down by a rubber band. And of course, they are needed to keep the dust out. My Aunt doesn't want dust getting into her water. Who would?

The problem is that even with using three bags a night, my Aunt is stockpiling bags rather rapidly. The drawers are full. I'm thinking of buying her a suitcase to keep the rest of her collection. But my Aunt doesn't approve of suitcases. Dust gets into them, she says. She admits that dust even gets into drawers. Which is why she gets the bags out every other day and dusts them. Gives them a careful dust, and then returns them to their correct drawer.

I believe my Aunt keeps these bags the way other old people have pets. Something to care for and look after. Not much company, perhaps. But at least house-trained. And, thankfully, very quiet.

2. Depressions

My Aunt and I suffered a great deal from depression, mostly hers. When she felt depressed she would come into my room – where I was usually looking at a blank sheet of paper, hoping a joke would appear on it – and sigh.

'What's the matter, Auntie?'

'I feel terrible.'

'Take a tranquillizer.'

'Do you think I should? Who knows what's in them?'

'Neither of us knows. Just take one and you'll feel better.'

'It may make me feel worse.'

'You always take them, and you always feel better.'

'I don't think they're the same ones as the last ones the doctor gave me.'

'Of course they are . . .'

'How do you know?'

'They look the same. Green and black. With your name on the bottle.'

'They don't taste the same. Perhaps the chemist has given me the wrong pills.'

'Take one, please . . .'

Sigh. 'You think I should?'

'Yes, I do.'

'Doctors. What do they know?'

As my Aunt got older she suffered more and more from hypochondria (which must be hereditary, because I get it too – especially in the middle of the night) and needed more and more to consult doctors, in spite of her basic lack of faith in them.

Days would start and end with my Aunt asking me to call a doctor because she felt 'terrible'. If the doctor came, she would repeat all her ailments and troubles. He would listen patiently, leave a prescription, and I would go to the chemist with it.

Whatever was prescribed, my Aunt would distrust it. Look at it, sniff it, and worry whether it would make her worse. She would snort. 'What do doctors know? My mother, bless her, knew more in her little finger than these young kids know in their whole heads . . .'

'Why get me to call the doctor then?'

'What do you want me to do? Suffer in silence?'

Whatever else my Aunt did, she certainly never suffered in silence. She suffered her anxieties and depressions out loud. She crossed each day gingerly, as if it were a tightrope which might snap under her at any moment, and plunge her to her death.

The mornings began with sighs and remarks about how badly she slept the night before.

'I went to bed late again last night,' she would say.

'Really, why?'

'I started thinking about your mother and how she never looked after herself properly. If she had listened to me, she would still be alive. Always rushing about, doing things, enjoying herself. She should have rested her heart more.'

'Well, she did live to be seventy-eight. That's not too bad.'

'She could have lived another twenty years, if she had listened to me.'

'Her doctor said . . .'

'What do doctors know? Nothing.'

Then came breakfast of cups of tea and cream crackers. (Always Jacobs'. I once tried to palm her off with another brand and she sulked all day.) Then more sighs and heartburn. Treatment for heartburn with fruit salts, and more cups of tea.

More heartburn would follow the cups of tea. More anxiety would follow the heartburn.

'Do you think I've got an ulcer?' she would ask me, clutching her stomach.

'Of course not. But I shouldn't drink so much tea. It can't be good for your stomach.'

'Perhaps I should see a Specialist?'

'What kind of Specialist?'

'Someone who specializes in everything.'

'Just take a tranquillizer.'

'Do you think I should?'

'Yes, for God's sake, yes.'

'It might make me feel worse . . .'

How I wished there was a pill she could have taken to make her calm enough to take her tranquillizers . . .

Once a week my Aunt would announce, 'I am going to have My Bath today.'

Now most people find it fairly simple to have a bath. You probably remember how it goes. You enter the bathroom, you put the plug in, turn on the hot water, get into the bath, wash, sing, get out, dry yourself and exit. My Aunt's approach was more Epic, like one of those long Eisenstein movies where people seem to be forever climbing up the same flight of stairs.

My Aunt would first slowly collect her clean linen, so as to have it all ready for changing into after Her Bath. This involved Sorting Out her linen, which took up most of the morning. Sometimes she would find an old letter buried amongst her linen, become interested in the memories it aroused and have to postpone The Bath until the next day. But if all went well, she would have a bite of lunch and start Phase Two around two o'clock.

Phase Two was Washing Out the Bath. She had a great fetish about cleanliness, which I imagine was sexual in origin, since she was a maiden Aunt. I am sure Freud would have enjoyed analysing her motives – all I know is that it was very heavy on the Vim. She would wash the bath very thoroughly, rinse it with running cold water, rewash it and then carefully feel the whole surface with her fingers. If there was the slightest blemish, she would clean the whole bath out again. This took about an hour. Then she would fill the bath.

By this time she was feeling a bit hungry and exhausted. So she would put on the kettle for a cup of tea. Several cups of tea and several cream crackers (her favourite food) later, she would go back to the bathroom. And find the water stone cold.

So she would have to empty the bath and re-fill it. While it was filling, she would go to collect her Clean Linen. She carried all her underclothes carefully wrapped up in an old piece of torn sheet, tied and sealed with several safety-pins. I don't know why they had to be wrapped up like this since the distance between her bedroom and the bathroom was all of five yards. I think it was in case dust (one of my Aunt's great enemies) got at the clean linen.

At last she was actually ready for Phase Three – the Bath itself. Before she entered the water, she would call out to me that she was going in (in case I had not noticed she was Having a Bath) and that she was leaving the door unlocked in case she felt faint and needed sudden rescuing from drowning.

I would then settle down to work, and she would call out again. 'Can you shut the window? I can't lift it and I can't have a draught blowing down on me in the bath.' She always liked the window open whilst running the bath, to allow the gas fumes from the Ascot to escape, and she would always then need the window shut before she could enjoy the bath.

About an hour later she would slowly emerge from the steamy bath-room, carefully swathed in clean underwear and towels. (For some other deep Freudian reason unknown to me, my Aunt never owned, and could never be persuaded to buy, any kind of dressing-gown. I think she thought they were only worn by Loose Women.)

'Be a good boy,' she would say, 'and make me a nice cup of tea. I feel faint. The bath was far too hot.' Or sometimes it was, 'I feel faint and cold. I think I caught a chill in there.'

I would make us a pot of tea and she would drink it greedily, and sigh, as if just rescued from a sinking ship. She looked rather like a survivor, all wrapped in towels and exuding dampness. 'Thank God that's done,' she said. 'It's a terrible business, having a bath.'

Calman and Women

But it's my turn
to leave you;

well—
If I allow myself to love you
I will be vulnerable and you
might hurt me— anyway..
I can't relate to you whilst
I am dependent on you financially..
I need to be free and I need
to love myself before I can
love you.. and my analyst says
that I am too anxious to love
anyone. I do love you, or rather,
I <u>want</u> to love you but..
Perhaps I could go and live away
from you for awhile, then I might
be free to come closer to you,
if you see what I mean...
Oh dear! It's really not fair
of you to keep asking me
these difficult questions...

Do you love me?

The Resident

WELL—
I'm here...

I wonder what he wants
me to do...

no sign of any instructions..

no message scrawled
in the dust..

It's really annoying -

I come here, I want to do
my best and
there's silence...

... Shall I dance?

Shall
I juggle?

or am I just going
to cope bravely
with life...

Condemned to my wheelchair...

resigned to my affliction..

Converting the
dross of pain
into the gold
of serenity...

No thank you...

it's a good
part but I hate
long runs...

THEN - I get these terrible
migraine headaches
once a month...

AND -
I don't sleep well -
if I get two or
three hours a
night I think
I'm lucky...

I just lie there worrying about the
money I owe and my
thinning hair...

AND THAT'S NOT ALL..

You see, basically I feel
I'm not really enjoying
life..

.. AND I worry
about that.

The joke is—
I didn't ask to be
here.. I was
created..

And it's not
funny...

... HOW WOULD
YOU LIKE TO
BE THE FIGMENT
OF SOMEONE ELSE'S
IMAGINATION?

I just skipped a page and
he didn't notice!

∴ AT LEAST —
I think he didn't notice... maybe
he intended me to skip a
page — part of some
terrible plot he's brewing...

You CANT
trust anyone
these days!

Ever since writers gave up
happy endings I feel very
uneasy...

It's become fashionable to be
unhappy. I'm old-fashioned.
I say - and I mean it ...

Let us remember—

BAD ART can be
GOOD FUN...

especially for us
poor souls who
have to sweat
it out..
day after day..

LIFT THAT ANGST!
TOTE THAT
PSYCHE!

Body & soul
racked with
pain...

SUDDENLY – I feel sad again..

I knew it was too good to last..

If he sees me enjoying myself he gets jealous...

WANTS ALL THE GLORY FOR HIMSELF...

I know what I'll do —

ILL RESIGN !

That will teach
him to mess me
about ...

A dignified letter —

Dear Sir, I feel
the time has come for us
to part company. I have
long felt intense
dissatisfaction with
the living arrangements.
Either it's too cold or too hot. It
rains frequently. The food is
inadequate — the company
non-existent. The fantasies I have
are of poor quality. One is continually
promised improvements in all directions.
Change is always in the air but never
on the ground. Even the misery lacks
grandeur. There is a feeling of triviality
infusing all departments. Apathy
and ennui are my handmaidens. I
would have thought you would have
been ashamed of the poverty of the
inventions I inhabit. I feel ashamed

to be seen in them. Fortunately, few people see me in my reduced circumstances, for the general public has the good taste to avoid the ridiculous and the insignificant. I therefore wish to be excused further participation in this charade. Please consider me as no longer available. I resign. I quit. I won't move. I won't speak your words. I won't perform your actions.
Thanking you for your interest, I remain,

Yours respectfully,

etc
etc

I think I just wrote myself out of a job..

- SILENCE -

I hope I didn't
hurt his feelings..

The great thing in this
racket is to
survive....

The next page
may be better..

and if it isn't..
don't worry..
keep smiling.. count
your blessings..
enjoy the little
things.. if the
text is lousy —
admire the
binding ...

As my mother used to say - if life hands you a lemon, make lemonade..

The trouble is -

lemonade gives me heartburn...

THE
END

Couples

The idea of a double-decker strip cartoon is not entirely new: in the early 1900s George Herriman created a double strip about a cat and a mouse living underneath a family called 'The Dingbat Family'. Eventually the family were evicted and the strip became 'Krazy Kat'.

I've always been interested in the gap between what people say and what they think, and I felt that a two-level strip might be a good place to explore this gap. At first I put the thoughts above the characters (as in the usual think-bubble convention), but as I wanted people to read the thoughts after they'd read the spoken words, I finally placed the thoughts on the bottom layer. My thoughts always seem to me to be below my conscious mind.

Originally I wanted to draw the bottom level as a rather surreal landscape, which only connected with the top level at times, and at other times followed its own logic. But various readers' reactions (the strip ran for a year in the *Sunday Times*) made me realize this would be too complicated and confusing. So the strip settled into something more conventional than I had hoped for – governed by the tyranny of a punch line in the last frame. I suppose the ideal strip would run on without having to end in a gag – but that would be something else. I think it's called 'life'.